CELEBRATION SERIES®

THE PIANO ODYSSEY®

PIANO
STUDIES / ETUDES

1

ISBN 0-88797-705-7

FREDERICK
HARRIS
MUSIC

CELEBRATION SERIES®
THE PIANO ODYSSEY®

The *Celebration Series®* was originally published in 1987 to international acclaim. In 1994, a second edition was released and received with heightened enthusiasm. Launched in 2001 and building on the success of previous editions, the *Celebration Series®, The Piano Odyssey®* takes advantage of the wealth of new repertoire and the changing interests and needs of teachers.

The series is breathtaking in its scope, presenting a true musical odyssey through the ages and their respective musical styles. The albums are graded from late elementary to early intermediate (albums Introductory to 3) through intermediate (albums 4 to 8) to advanced and concert repertoire (albums 9 and 10). Each volume of repertoire comprises a carefully selected grouping of pieces from the Baroque, Classical, Romantic, and 20th-century style periods. *Studies/Etudes* albums present compositions especially suited for building technique as well as musicality relevant to the repertoire of each level. *Student Workbooks* and recordings are available to assist in the study and enjoyment of the music. In addition, the comprehensive *Handbook for Teachers* is an invaluable pedagogical resource.

A Note on Editing and Performance Practice

Most Baroque and early Classical composers wrote few dynamics, articulation, or other performance indications in their scores. Interpretation was left up to the performer, with the expectation that the performance practice was understood. In this edition, therefore, most of the dynamics and tempo indications in the Baroque and early Classical pieces have been added by the editors. These editorial markings, including fingering and the execution of ornaments, are intended to be helpful rather than definitive.

The keyboard instruments of the 17th and early 18th centuries lacked the sustaining power of the modern piano. Consequently, the usual keyboard touch was detached rather than legato. The pianist should assume that a lightly detached touch is appropriate for Baroque and early Classical music, unless a different approach is indicated by the style of the music.

Even into the 19th century, composers' scores could vary from copy to copy or edition to edition. Thus, the editors of the *Celebration Series®* have also made editorial choices in much of the Classical and Romantic repertoire presented in the series.

This edition follows the policy that the bar line cancels accidentals. In accordance with current practice, cautionary accidentals are added only in cases of possible ambiguity.

Teachers and students should refer to the companion guides – the *Student Workbooks* and the *Handbook for Teachers* – for further discussion of style and pedagogical elements. For examination requirements of The Royal Conservatory of Music, please refer to the current *Piano Syllabus*.

Dr. Trish Sauerbrei
Editor-in-Chief

Contents

Study no. 1: Robins	*Linda Niamath*	4
Study no. 2: A Porcupine Dance, op. 89, no. 8	*Dmitri Kabalevsky*	4
Study no. 3: Study in C Major, op. 777, no. 3	*Carl Czerny*	5
Study no. 4: Morning Greeting, op. 117, no. 13	*Cornelius Gurlitt*	6
Study no. 5: Martellato and Forte–Piano	*Lajos Papp*	7
Study no. 6: Hunting Horns	*Theodor Oesten*	8
Study no. 7: Both Ways	*Alexandre Tansman*	9
Study no. 8: The Bear	*Vladimir Ivanovich Rebikov*	10
Study no. 9: Kites	*Linda Niamath*	12
Study no. 10: Prelude for Aries	*Terry Winter Owens*	13
Study no. 11: Ins and Outs	*Paul Sheftel*	14
Study no. 12: Little Mouse	*Jerzy Lefeld*	15
Study no. 13: Woodland Scene	*Leon Aubry*	16

Study no. 1

Robins

Linda Niamath
(1939 –   )

Study no. 2

A Porcupine Dance

op. 89, no. 8

Dmitri Kabalevsky
(1904 – 1987)

Study no. 3

Study in C Major
op. 777, no. 3

Carl Czerny
(1791 – 1857)

Allegro ♩ = 152 – 168

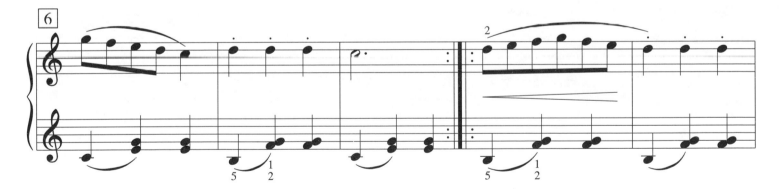

Source: 24 *Five-Finger Exercises*, op. 777

0-88797-705-7 / 05

Study no. 4

Morning Greeting
op. 117, no. 13

Cornelius Gurlitt
(1820 – 1901)

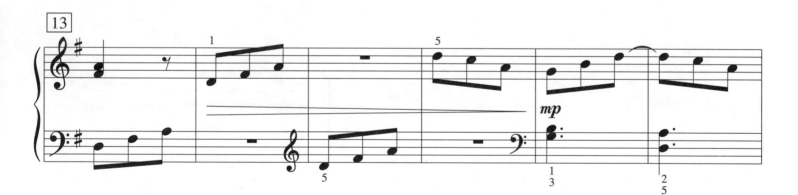

Original title: "Morgengruss"
Source: *The First Lessons: 34 Short Pieces for the Pianoforte*, op. 117

Study no. 5

Martellato

Lajos Papp
(1935 –   )

(a) Press keys down silently and hold throughout.
For examinations, *Martellato* and *Forte-Piano* are to be played as one selection.

Forte–Piano

Lajos Papp
(1935 –   )

(a) Press keys down silently and hold throughout.
For examinations, *Martellato* and *Forte–Piano* are to be played as one selection.

Source: *27 Small Piano Pieces*

Study no. 6

Hunting Horns

Theodor Oesten
(1813 – 1870)

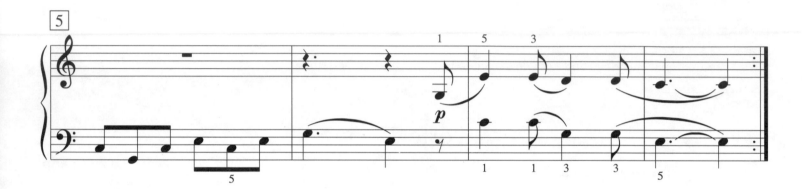

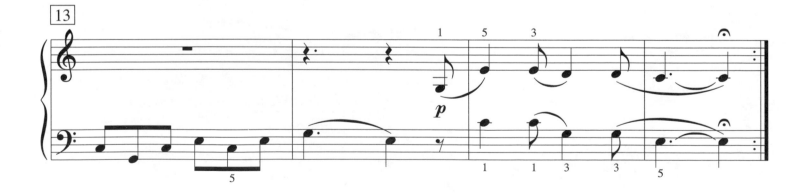

Study no. 7

Both Ways

Alexandre Tansman
(1897– 1986)

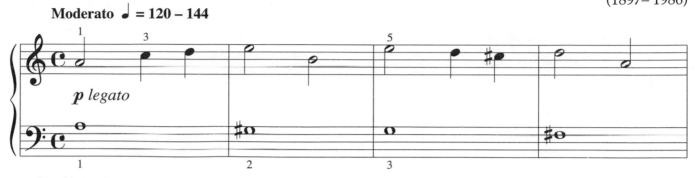

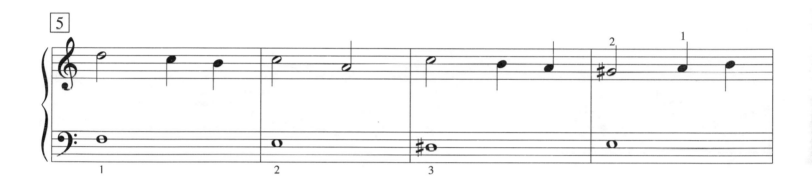

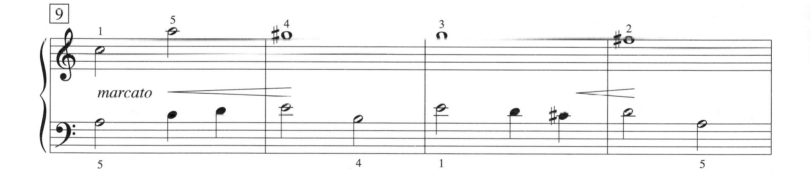

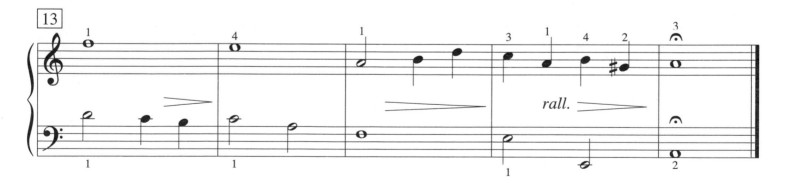

Source: *On s'amuse au piano*

Study no. 8

The Bear

Vladimir Ivanovich Rebikov
(1866 – 1920)

Source: *Christmas Gifts*

Study no. 9

Kites

Linda Niamath
(1939 –   )

Smoothly and freely ♩ = 112 – 126

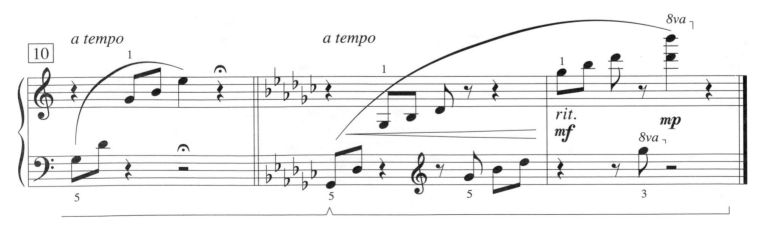

Source: *All Year Round*

© Copyright 1998 The Frederick Harris Music Co., Limited, Mississauga, Ontario, Canada.

Study no. 10

Prelude for Aries

Terry Winter Owens
(1935 –   )

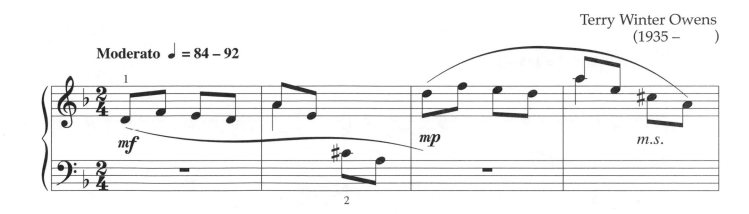

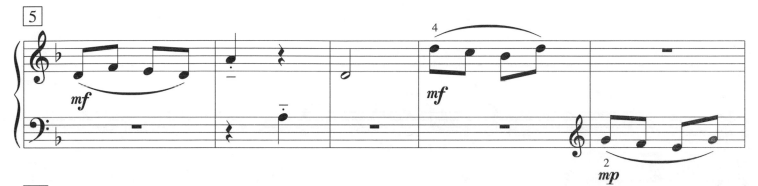

Source: *Astrological Preludes*

Study no. 11

Ins and Outs ✧

Paul Sheftel
(1933 –   )

Not fast ♩ = 108 – 116

Source: *Keyboard Challenges: Thirteen Elementary Level Solos*

Study no. 12

Little Mouse

Jerzy Lefeld

Allegro moderato ♩ = 96 – 104

Study no. 13

Woodland Scene

Leon Aubry